BEATLEMANIA
1963~1966

CONTENTS

ISBN 0-88188-591-6

7777 West Bluemound Road P.O. Box 13819 Milwaukee, WI 53213

ALL MY LOVING

Words and Music by JOHN LENNON
and PAUL McCARTNEY

Bb7
Eb
Cm
Ab
way I'll write home ev - 'ry day and I'll send ALL MY
LOV - ING to you. I'll pre - ALL MY
1
2
G+
LOV - ING, I will send to you. ALL MY
LOV - ING, Dar - ling I'll be true.

AND I LOVE HER

Words and Music by JOHN LENNON
and PAUL McCARTNEY

1.
2.
Eb
Cm
Gm
Bb7
C
A love like ours
Could nev - er die
As long as I have you near me.
D.S. al Coda
CODA

BABY'S IN BLACK

Words and Music by JOHN LENNON
and PAUL McCARTNEY

G
D
A7
1. D
2. D
Ab
Eb
Bb7
Eb
Eb
though he'll nev - er come back, she's dressed in black.
though it's on - ly a whim, she thinks of
him.
Bm7
E7
G
A7
Cm7
F7
Ab
Bb7
Oh, how long will it take till she sees the mis - take she has
D
A7
G7
A7
Eb
Bb7
Ab7
Bb7
made? Dear, what can I do? Ba - by's in black and I'm feel - ing blue. Tell me
D
G
D
A7
D
Eb
Ab
Eb
Bb7
Eb
oh, what can I do?
She thinks of him and

D7
Eb7
G
Ab
G
Ab
D
Eb
A7
Bb7
so she dress - es in black. And though he'll nev - er come back she's dressed in
D
Eb
D
Eb
A7
Bb7
black. Oh dear, what can I do?
G7
Ab7
A7
Bb7
D
Eb
G
Ab
D
Eb
G
Ab
D
Eb
Ba - by's in black and I'm feel - ing blue. Tell me oh what can I do?

FOR NO ONE

Words and Music by JOHN LENNON
and PAUL McCARTNEY

A7 Dm A7
love be - hind the tears cried for no - one
Dm A7 Dm
A love that should have last - ed years
G7 sus 4 G7 C Em
You want her you need her
You stay home she goes out
Your day breaks your mind aches
Am C F
and yet you don't be - lieve her when she says her love
she says that long a - go she knew some - one but now
there will be times when all the things you said will fill

B♭
C
to Coda
1.
2.
D.S. al Coda
is dead you think she needs you And in her
he's gone she does - n't need him
your head you won't for - get her
Coda
C
Dm
A7
And in her eyes you see noth-ing
Dm
A7
Dm
A7
no sign of love be - hind the tears cried for no one
Dm
A7
Dm
G7sus4
G7
a love that should have last - ed years.
rit.

CAN'T BUY ME LOVE

Words and Music by JOHN LENNON
and PAUL McCARTNEY

G
F7
C
To Coda
I don't care too much for mon-ey for mon-ey Can't Buy Me Love. I'll
C
Em
Am
C
Can't Buy Me Love Ev - 'ry-bod-y tells me so
C
Em
Am
Dm7
G7
D. S. al Coda
Can't Buy Me Love No no no no
Coda
C
Em
Am
Em
Can't Buy Me Love Love
Am
Dm7
G7
C
Can't Buy Me Love

DAY TRIPPER

Words and Music by JOHN LENNON
and PAUL McCARTNEY

F
E7
A
G
so long to find out, and I found out.
C
3rd Time
To Coda
G
Ah
Fmaj7
G7
G
Fmaj7
G
D.C. al Coda
Ah
Coda
C
C
Repeat and fade
Day Trip-per,
Day Trip-per, Yeh.

DRIVE MY CAR

Words and Music by JOHN LENNON
and PAUL McCARTNEY

C7
Em
Yes, I'm gon-na be a star. —
Ba - by, you can drive my car, —
C
D
Dm7
To Coda
1.
2.
— and may-be I'll love — you".
Beep Beep Mm Beep Beep, Yeah! —
C
F
Em
C7
"Ba-by, you can drive my car,
Yes, I'm gon-na be a star. —
— Ba - by, you can drive my car, — and may-be I'll love — you".
D
D. S. al Coda
Coda
Beep Beep Mm Beep Beep, Yeah! —
Repeat and fade

EIGHT DAYS A WEEK

Words and Music by JOHN LENNON
and PAUL McCARTNEY

B♭
C7
E♭
To Coda
1.
2.3.
Ain't got noth-in' but love babe,
(girl,)
Eight days a week.
F
Gm
Eight days a week I love you.
C7
E♭6
F7
D. S. al ⊕ Coda
Eight days a week is not e - nough to show I care.
Coda
Eight days a week,
Eight days a week.
Cm7
cresc.
f

ELEANOR RIGBY

C
wear-ing the face that she keeps in a jar by the door,
darn-ing his socks in the night when there's no - bod-y there,
wip-ing the dirt from his hands as he walks from the grave,
Em
Em7
Em6
C
who is it for?
what does he care?
no one was saved.
All the lone - ly peo - ple, where do they all come from?
Em
Em7
Em6
C
All the lone - ly peo - ple, where do they all be-long?
To Coda
To Coda
Em
Em
1.
2.
D.C. al Coda
Coda
Em

EVERY LITTLE THING

Words and Music by JOHN LENNON
and PAUL McCARTNEY

D
C
D
C D
Eb
Db
to Coda
Eb
Db Eb
And you know the things she does, she does for me,__ yeah,__
D
G A7
D
Eb
Ab Bb7
Eb
When I'm with her I'm hap - py Just to know that she
There is one thing I'm sure of I will love her for -
C G
Em7
A7
D
Db Ab
Fm7
Bb7
Eb
D.S. al Coda
loves_ me, Yes, I know that she loves me now._
ev - er, For I know love will nev - er die.__
C D C D
G A7
D
Coda Db Eb Db Eb
Ab Bb7
Eb
Repeat and Fade
me__ oo__ Ev-'ry lit-tle thing__

FROM A WINDOW

Words and Music by JOHN LENNON
and PAUL McCARTNEY

1.
2.
Am7
G
C
sight.
one.
Oh, I would be glad
D7
G
G7
just to have a love like that;
C
B7
Em
Oh, I would be true and I'd live my life for
A7
D7
G
you. So meet me to-night just where the light

Em
Am7
shines from a win - dow,
And as I take your
D7
to Coda
G
D.S. al Coda
hand say that you'll be mine to - night
Coda
E♭
you'll be mine to -
C
G
night.
3
3

GIRL

Words and Music by JOHN LENNON
and PAUL McCARTNEY

Dm
Fm
Am
Cm
C
E♭
Em
Gm
Still you don't re - gret a sin - gle day.
Af - ter all this time I don't know why.
Will she still be - lieve it when he's dead.
Ah, Girl,
Dm
Fm
G7
B♭7
C
E♭
Em
Gm
to Coda
oothss (Breathe in) Girl, Girl.
1. Dm7
Fm7
G7
B♭7
2. When I
2. Dm7
Fm7
G7
B♭7
Dm
Fm7
A
C
She's the kind of girl who puts you down, When friends are there, you feel a
Dm7
Fm7
A
C
Dm7
Fm7
fool. (Tu tu tu tu tu tu tu tu tu tu tu tu)
When you say she's look - ing good, She
3

A
C
Dm7
Fm7
F
A♭
acts as if it's un - der - stood, She's cool ooh ooh ooh
C
E♭
Em
Gm
Dm7
Fm7
G7
B♭7
Dm
Fm
D.S. 𝄋 al ⊕ Coda
Girl. oothss (Breathe in) Girl, Girl. 3. Was she
⊕ Coda
Am
Cm
E7
G7
1. C
2. Am
Repeat and Fade
Ah, Girl. oothss (Breathe in)

GOOD DAY SUNSHINE

Words and Music by JOHN LENNON
and PAUL McCARTNEY

E7
A
A
2.
D
B7
I'm in love and it's a sun-ny day.
touch the ground.
(Solo)
f
E
A
D
A
3.
lov - ing me.
She feels good,
(trem. ad lib.)
(trem. ad lib.)
F#7
B7
E7
A
D. S. al Coda
she knows she's look-ing fine,
I'm so proud to know that she is mine.
Coda
E7
B
F#7
B
F#7
shine
Good day sun - shine.
Good day sun -
E7
F7
shine,
Good day sun - shine,
Good day sun - shine,
(repeat and fade)

GOT TO GET YOU INTO MY LIFE

Words and Music by JOHN LENNON
and PAUL McCARTNEY

C
Am7
D
G
ev - 'ry sin - gle day of my life?
say we'll be to - geth - er ev - 'ry day.
ev - 'ry sin - gle day of my life?
(Shout)
D7
Got to get you in - to my life!
(Solo)
ff
To Coda
D. S. al Coda
Coda
(No Chords)
Got to get you in - to my life!
D. C. and fade after 4 bars.

A HARD DAY'S NIGHT

Words and Music by JOHN LENNON
and PAUL McCARTNEY

Am
Em
C
ev-'ry-thing seems _ to be al-right.
When I'm home ___
Am
F6
G7
D. S. al ⊕ Coda
feel-ing you hold - ing me tight,
tight.
Yeah, ___ 3. It's been a
⊕ Coda
C
F
C
F7
C
F
right.
You know I feel ___
al - right ___
You know I
C
F7
Bb6
C
feel al - right. ___

HELP!

Words and Music by JOHN LENNON
and PAUL McCARTNEY

Em
C
F
G
Am
Now I find I've changed my mind, I've o-pened up the doors.
I know that I just need you like I've nev-er done be-fore.
Help me if you
can. I'm feel-ing down
And I do ap-pre-ci-ate you be-ing 'round.
D7
Help me get my feet back on the ground.
Won't you please,
1.2.
please help me?
3.
please help me? Help me! Help me! Oo.

HERE, THERE AND EVERYWHERE

Words and Music by JOHN LENNON
and PAUL McCARTNEY

F♯m7 B7 F♯m7 B7 Em Am Am7 D7 F7
it can be; Some-one is speak - ing but she does-n't know he's there. I want her
B♭ Gm Cm D7 Gm Cm7 D7
ev-'ry-where and if she's be-side me I know I need nev-er care. But to love her is to meet her
mf
G Am7 Bm C G Am7 Bm7 C
ev-'ry-where, know-ing that love is to share; Each one be-liev - ing that love
mp
F♯m7 B7 F♯m7 B7 Em Am Am7 D7 F7
1.
never dies, watch-ing her eyes and hop - ing I'm al - ways there. I want her
Am7 D7sus G Am Bm C G Am7 Bm C G
2.
To be there and ev - 'ry-where, here, there and ev - 'ry-where.

HOLD ME TIGHT

Words and Music by
McCARTNEY

Fm
C
Fm
C
night, it's you, you, you, you - oo - oo - oo
1. G7
2. Eb
C
Eb
oo. oo. Don't know what it means to
C
F
Dm
D7
hold you tight, be - ing here a - lone to - night with you. It
G7
D.S. al Coda
Coda
Eb
C
Eb
rit.
C
feels so right now, oo - oo - oo, you - oo - oo.
rit.

I CALL YOUR NAME

Words and Music by JOHN LENNON
and PAUL McCARTNEY

C
F
Am
on. Well don't you know I can't take it, I don't know who can,
D7
Fm
G7
I'm not goin' to Ma-ya-yake it I'm not that kind of man. Oh I can't
C7
A7
D7
sleep at night, But just the same I nev-er weep at night
1.
2.
C
F
I call your name. I call your name I call your name.

I DON'T WANT TO SPOIL THE PARTY

Words and Music by JOHN LENNON
and PAUL McCARTNEY

C
Bb
C
4th time to Coda
1.
2. 3.
Dm7
G7
turns up while I'm gone, Please let me know.
think I'll take a walk and look for her.
turns up while I'm gone, please let me know.
think I'll take a walk and look for her.
2. I've
4. I've
Though to-night
C
Am7
D7
F
she's made me sad, I still love
G7
Dm7
G7
C
Am7
D7
her. If I find her I'll be glad, I still
F
G7
Dm7
G7
love her. 3. I don't
D. S. al Coda
Coda
C
G7
C
C7
C6
G7
Gm
Dm
G7
C

I FEEL FINE

Words and Music by JOHN LENNON
and PAUL McCARTNEY

F
Am
Bb
Gm7
C7
I'm so glad that she's my lit-tle girl.
She's so glad she's
telling all the world
That her ba-by buys her things you know. He buys her dia-mond rings
F7
you know, She said so.
C
Bb7
She's in love with me and I Feel Fine.
She's in love with me and I Feel Fine.

IF I FELL

Words and Music by JOHN LENNON
and PAUL McCARTNEY

F7
Bb 6 fr
Cm 3 fr
Dm 5 fr
Db° 5 fr
must be sure from the ve - ry start that
run and hide if I love you too oh
Cm7 3 fr
F7 6 fr
1. Bb 6 fr
Ebm 6 fr
F7
you would love me more than her
please don't hurt my pride like her
If I
2. Bb9
Bb9
Eb 3 fr
her 'Cos I could - n't stand the pain
And I
Ebm 6 fr
Bb 6 fr
F7
would be sad if our new love was in vain
So I

Bb
6 fr
Cm
3 fr
Dm
5 fr
Db°
5 fr
Cm7
3 fr
F7
hope you see that I would love to love you
Bb
6 fr
Cm7
3 fr
Dm
5 fr
Db°
Cm7
3 fr
To Coda
F7
Bb7
D.S. al Coda
and that she will cry when she learns we are two
'Cos I
F7
Coda
Bb
6 fr
Ebm
6 fr
she learns we are two
If I fell in love with
Bb
6 fr
Ebm
6 fr
Bb
6 fr
you.

I'LL BE BACK

Words and Music by JOHN LENNON
and PAUL McCARTNEY
G
You know
Gm
B♭
F
E♭
if you break my heart I'll go But I'll
You could find bet - ter things to do Than to
You could find bet - ter things to do Than to
D7
C
D7
G
Gm
be back a - gain 'Cos I told you
break my heart a - gain This time I will
break my heart a - gain This time I will
B♭
F
E♭
D7
C
D7
G
once be - fore good - bye But I came back a - gain
try to show that I'm Not try - ing to pre - tend
try to show that I'm Not try - ing to pre - tend

1.
G
Em
Am
I love you so oh
I wan-na go
I'm the one who wants you
But I hate to leave you
Am
D7
C
D7
C
D7
To Coda
Yes I'm the one who wants you oh ho oh ho Oh
You know I hate to leave you oh ho oh ho
2.
G
Am
C+
Am7
Bm
I thought that you would re-al-ize
Bm
Em
A7
C
That if I ran a-way from you that you would want me too But I've got a big sur-prise

D
C
D
C
D7
D.S. % al Coda
Oh ho Oh ho Oh
Coda
D7
Gm
B♭
F
Oh You if you break my heart I'll go
E♭
D7
C
G
But I'll be back a - gain.
G
Gm
Repeat and Fade

I'LL CRY INSTEAD

Words and Music by JOHN LENNON
and PAUL McCARTNEY

F
C7
up — to - day — But I can't —
say it some - how — But I can't —
man — can do — Un - til then —
So I Cry — In -
So I Cry — In -
I'll cry — In -
1.
2. To next strain
3. Fine
F
Bb
stead.
2. I've got a
stead.
Don't want to
stead.
Am
G7
cry when there's peo-ple there, — I get shy when they start to stare; — I'm
C
Dm
D.S. al Fine
gon-na hide my-self a - way, — ay, hay; — But I'll come back a - gain some day, — And when I

I'LL FOLLOW THE SUN

Words and Music by JOHN LENNON
and PAUL McCARTNEY

Bm7
Dm6
A
A7
Cm7
E♭m6
B♭
B♭7
time has come, and so, my love, I must go
And though I
Bm7
Dm6
A
Bm7
Cm7
E♭m6
B♭
Cm7
lose a friend
In the end you will know,
Oh,
E7
D7
A
B7
F7
E♭7
B♭
C7
One day
you'll find
that I have gone
But to-
A
C♯m
B7
E7
A
E11
D
A
B♭
Dm
C7
F7
B♭
F11
E♭
B♭
mor-row may rain
so
I'll fol-low the sun.

I'M A LOSER

Words and Music by JOHN LENNON
and PAUL McCARTNEY

2. She was a girl
In a million, my friend
I should have known
She would win in the end.

3. Although I laugh
And I act like a clown
Beneath this mask
I am wearing a frown.

4. My tears are falling
Like rain from the sky
Is it for her
Or myself that I cry.

5. What have I done
To deserve such a fate
I realize
I have left it too late.

6. And so it's true
Pride comes before a fall
I'm telling you
So that you won't lose all.

I'M HAPPY JUST TO DANCE WITH YOU

Words and Music by JOHN LENNON
and PAUL McCARTNEY

hap-py just to dance with you. I don't you. Just to
dance with you Is ev-'ry-thing I
need. Be-fore this dance is through I think I'll love you too, I'm so
hap-py when you dance with me. If some-bod-y tries to take my place

Fm7
B♭7
E♭
G♭dim
Fm7
B♭7
Let's pre - tend we just can't see his face.
In this
A♭
E♭
Cm
A♭
B♭+
world there's noth-ing I would rath-er do
'Cos I'm hap-py just to dance with
I've dis - cov-ered I'm in love with
1. E♭
you. Just to
2. Cm
you.
Fm7
Gm
Oh, oh, 'Cos I'm hap-py just to dance with
A♭
B♭+
Cm
you.
Fm7
Gm
Oh, oh,
A♭6
B♭7
Oh, oh,
E♭
Oh.

I'M LOOKING THROUGH YOU

Words and Music by JOHN LENNON
and PAUL McCARTNEY

G C Am7 C7 G7 C
I'm Look - ing Through You_ you're not_ the same.
I'm Look - ing Through You_ you're not_ the same.
G7 C G7 C G C C
Why, tell me
G C
why did you not treat me right?_ Love has a
G D G C
nas - ty hab - it of dis - ap - pear - ing o - ver - night. You're think - ing

Am7
Em
D
G
C
of me in the same old way. You were a -
Am7
Em
D
Em
bove me but not to - day. The on - ly
D
C
G
C
D
G
C
Am7
dif - f'rence is you're down there. I'm Look - ing Through You
C7
G7
C
G7
C
G7
C
G7
C
Repeat and fade
and you're no - where.

IN MY LIFE

Words and Music by JOHN LENNON
and PAUL McCARTNEY

G
Em7
A7
Cm
still can re-call. Some are dead and some are liv-ing, In my life I've
went be-fore. I know I'll of-ten stop and think a-bout them, In my life I'll
G
D
D
G
1.
2.
loved them all.
love you more.
2. But of
Though I
Em7
C
F
G
know I'll nev-er lose af-fec-tion for peo-ple and things that went be-fore I
Em7
A7
Cm
G
know I'll of-ten stop and think a-bout them, In my life I'll love you more.
D
G
D
D7
G
ten. ten.
In my life I'll love you more.

I SHOULD HAVE KNOWN BETTER

Words and Music by JOHN LENNON
and PAUL McCARTNEY

Am
F
C
E7
That when I tell you that I love you, oh,
Am
C
You're gon - na say you love me too, Hoo, hoo, hoo, hoo Oh,
3
F
G
C
Am
And when I ask you to be mine,
F
G7
C
G7
1.
C
G7
D.S. al Fine
You're gon - na say you love me too.
3. So, I
2. Fine
C
G7
You love me too,
You love me too.

IT'S FOR YOU

Words and Music by JOHN LENNON
and PAUL McCARTNEY

Fm6
G+
G7
Cm
They said that love was a lie
Told me that I
F
Fm
Cm
should nev-er try to find
Some-bod-y who'd be kind
Fm6
G7
Fm6
G7
Kind to on-ly me
So I just
Cm
F
tell them they're right
Who wants a fight?
Tell them I quite a-gree

Fm
Cm
Fm6
D.S. 𝄋 al Coda
No-bod-y'd love me Then I look at you And
Coda
Eb
Ab maj7
Db maj7
Gm7
It's for you It's for
you It's for
Cm
Gm7
you.
f

IT'S ONLY LOVE

Words and Music by JOHN LENNON
and PAUL McCARTNEY

G11 3 fr. G7 G7+ C F
dries Butter-flies why I am so
bright Very bright haven't I the
G C Am
shy when I'm be-side you It's on-ly
right to make it up girl
B♭ G7 C
love and that is all Why should I feel the way I do
Am B♭ G7
It's on-ly love and that is all But it's so

F
1. G7
2. G7
hard lov - ing you you Yes it's so
F
G7
C
hard lov - ing you lov - ing you.
Am
C
Am
C
Am
C

IT WON'T BE LONG

Words and Music by
PAUL McCARTNEY

to Coda
C
Am
yeh yeh yeh It won't be long, yeh yeh yeh yeh yeh yeh It won't be long yeh yeh Till
F D7 G9 C
I be - long to you. Since you left me
G+ Gm6 A7 F
I'm so a - lone Now you're com-ing, you're com-ing on home. I'll be good like I
G7 Dm7 Dm
1 G7
2 G7
know I should You're com-ing home, you're com - ing home. home.
3
D.S. al Coda
F
rit.
Eb D7 Dbmaj7 Cmaj7
I be - long to you.
CODA

LITTLE CHILD

Words and Music by JOHN LENNON
and PAUL McCARTNEY

D7
G7
mine, all mine. So come on, come on, come on.
on, come on. So come on, come on, come on.
Lit - tle Child,
C7
C7
F
C7
Lit- tle Child,
Lit-tle Child
Won't you dance with me
G7
F
D9
G7
C
To Coda
D.S. al Coda
I'm so sad and lone - ly
Ba - by take a chance with me.
2. When you're
Coda
C
A7
D9
G7
C
Oh yeh
Ba - by take a chance with me.

MICHELLE

Words and Music by JOHN LENNON
and PAUL McCARTNEY

Cm
F7
B♭
A
Dm
Gm
That's all I want to say. Un-til I find a way I will
I need to make you see what you mean to me. Un-
I think you know by now. I'll get to you some - how. Un-
Dm
C♯+
Dm7
Dm6
Gm6
A
A
To Coda
1.
2.
D. S. al ⊕ Coda
say the on - ly words I know that you'll, un - der - stand.
til I do, I'm hop - ing you will know what I mean. I
til I do, I'm tell - ing you, so you'll un - der -
Coda
A
D
Gm
B♭
C
B♭
stand. Mi - chelle ma belle sont les mots qui vont tres bien en -
mf
A
B♭
A
B♭
Dm
Gm
semble, tres bien en - semble. I will say the on - ly words I know that you'll un - der-
A
D
Gm7
C7
B♭
A
stand, my Mi - chelle.

THE NIGHT BEFORE

Words and Music by JOHN LENNON
and PAUL McCARTNEY

Bb
Eb7
Bb
Db
Cm7
1.
Treat me like you did the night be-fore.
Db
Bb
2. To next strain
3. Fine
Like the night be - fore.
Fm7
Fm7-5
Bb7
Eb
Last night is the night I will re - mem - ber you by.
Gm7
C7
F7
D.S. al Fine
When I think of things we did It makes me wan-na cry.

NO REPLY

Words and Music by JOHN LENNON
and PAUL McCARTNEY

Em
Bm
Cmaj7
Bm
I saw the light I know that you saw
I near - ly died 'Cos you walked hand in
Am7
D7
G
to Coda
me 'cos I looked up to see your face
hand with an - oth - er man in my place
1. G
2. G
G
B7
I tried to tel - e -
If I were you I'd re - al - ise that
E
Am
C
I love you more than an - y oth - er

G
G
G
B7
guy
And I'll for - give
the
lies
that
E
Am
C
I
heard
be - fore
When you
gave
me
no
re -
G
D.S. al Coda
Coda
G
ply
I
tried
to
tel - e -
No
re - ply
Em
Bm
Cmaj7
No re - ply.

TELL ME WHAT YOU SEE

Words and Music by JOHN LENNON
and PAUL McCARTNEY

C
D7
D11
G
C
If I'm part - of you
I'll make bright - your day
Try - in' to get to you
O - pen up - your eyes -
Look in - to - these eyes -
O - pen up your eyes -
G
C
G
- now -
Tell me what - you see
C
G
C
To Coda
G
It is no - sur - prise - now -
What you see - is me
Don't you re - a - lise - now -
It is no sur - prise - now -

G9
C
Tell me what you see
solo
G
D7
G
G
D.S.
Coda
G
G9
mm mm
G9
C
mm mm mm
solo

NORWEGIAN WOOD
(THIS BIRD HAS FLOWN)

Words and Music by JOHN LENNON
and PAUL McCARTNEY

Gm
Am7
D7
I looked a - round and I no - ticed there was - n't a chair.
told her I did - n't and crawled off to sleep in the bath.
G
To Coda
I sat on a rug bi - ding my time, drink - ing her wine,
And when I a - woke I was a - lone, this bird had flown,
We talked un - til two and then she said "It's time for bed."
So I lit a fire, Is - n't it good Nor - we - gian Wood.
She
D. S. al Coda
Coda

NOWHERE MAN

Words and Music by JOHN LENNON
and PAUL McCARTNEY

Gm
Ab
4th Fret
Gm
Ab
4th Fret
please lis-ten, You don't know what you're miss-ing, No-where Man.
don't wor-ry, Take your time, Don't hur-ry, Leave it all
Gm
Ab
4th Fret
Bb7
The world is at your com-mand.
till some-bod-y else lends you a hand.
Coda
Eb
Ab
4th Fret
Abm
4th Fret
Ab
4th Fret
Eb
Mak-ing all his no-where plans for no - bod - y.
Ab
4th Fret
Abm
4th Fret
Eb
Mak-ing all his no-where plans for no-bod-y.
rit.

PAPERBACK WRITER

Words and Music by JOHN LENNON
and PAUL McCARTNEY

dirt - y sto-ry of a dirt - y man, and his cling - ing wife does-n't un-der-stand. His
real - ly like it you can have the rights, It could make a mil-lion for you ov-er-night. If you
son is work-ing for the Dail-y Mail; It's a stead -y job But he wants to be a pa-per-back
must re - turn it you can send it here, But I need a break and I want to be a pa-per-back
C
G7
writ - er, pa - per-back writ - er.
writ - er, pa - per-back writ - er.
2nd time
D.C. al ♦ Coda
♦ Coda
G7
Pa - per-back writ - er,
Fade

RAIN

Words and Music by JOHN LENNON
and PAUL McCARTNEY

G
mind.
Shine,
C
G
the weath-er's fine.
I can show you that
Can you hear me that
C
D
G
when it starts to rain
when it rains and shines
C
D
G
ev - 'ry-thing's the same.
it's just a state of mind.
C
I can show you.
Can you hear me?
G5
I can show
Can you hear
1.
you.
2.
me?

THIS BOY
(RINGO'S THEME)

Words and Music by JOHN LENNON
and PAUL McCARTNEY

G
E7
A7
That boy won't be hap-py till he's seen you cry.
3
D
Bm
Em
A7
This boy would-n't mind the pain,
Would al-ways feel the
mp
same, if this boy gets you back a-gain.
G
This boy,
this boy.
Fade out on repeat
p

RUN FOR YOUR LIFE

Medium Beat

Words and Music by JOHN LENNON
and PAUL McCARTNEY

3. Let this be a sermon,
I mean everything I said.
Baby, I'm determined,
And I'd rather see you dead.

Chos. You'd better run for your life
If you can, little girl.
Hide your head in the sand, little girl.
If I catch you with another man
That's the end –ah, little girl.

4. I'd rather see you dead, little girl,
Than to be with another man.
You'd better keep your head, little girl,
Or I won't know where I am.

Chos. You'd better run for your life
If you can, little girl.
Hide you head in the sand, little girl.
If I catch you with another man
That's the end –ah, little girl.

SHE'S A WOMAN

Words and Music by JOHN LENNON
and PAUL McCARTNEY

Eb7
Bb7
Fm7
Bb7
Ab7
Ebm7
Turn me on when I get lone - ly, Peo - ple tell me
She will nev - er make me jeal - ous, Gives me all her
Ab7
Eb7
Ab7
Eb7
Bb7
1.
that she's on - ly fool - in', I know she is - n't.
time as well as lov - in', Don't ask me why.
Eb7
Gm
C7
Gm
2.3.
She's a wo - man who un - der-stands,
She's a wo - man who
Ab
Bb7
Eb7
Eb7
Repeat and fade
Ebm7
4.
3
loves her man;
She's a wo - man,
She's a

TELL ME WHY

Words and Music by JOHN LENNON
and PAUL McCARTNEY

G7
If you'll on - ly lis - ten to my pleas,
Is there
Am
Dm
an - y - thing I can do?
'Cos I real - ly can't stand it, I'm
G7
Dm7
G7
C
Am
Dm7
G7
So in love with you.
Tell me
D.S. al Coda
CODA
G7
Dm7
G7
Am
A♭
G9
G7
C
lied to me.

Dm7 G7 C
1. 2.
Well, I gave you ev - 'ry - thing I had
If it's some - thing that I've said or done
Am Dm7 G7
But you left me sit - ting on my own. Did you have
Tell me what and I'll ap - ol - o - gise. If you don't,
C Am Dm7
to treat me oh, so bad? All I do is hang my head and moan.
I real - ly can't go on Hold - ing back these tears in my eyes.
G7 C7 F7
3
Tell me
Well, I beg you on my bend - ed knees,

THINGS WE SAID TODAY

Words and Music by JOHN LENNON
and PAUL McCARTNEY

Am Em7 Am C
Gm Dm7 Gm B♭
some - how I will know. Some - day when I'm
seems so hard to find. Some - day when we're
we'll go on and on. Some - day when we're
C7 F B♭
B♭7 E♭ A♭
lone - ly wish - ing you weren't so far a - way,
dream - ing deep in love not a lot to say,
dream - ing deep in love not a lot to say,
Am Em7 Am Em7 Am Em7
Gm Dm7 Gm Dm7 Gm Dm7 To Coda
Then I will re - mem - ber
Then we will re - mem - ber Things We Said To - day.
Then we will re - mem - ber
1. Am
Gm
2. A
G

A
D7
C7
Me, I'm just the luck - y kind,
B7
A7
E7
D7
Love to hear you say that love is love,
A
G
D7
C7
And though we may be blind,
B7
A7
B♭
A♭
D.S. al Coda
Love is here to stay and that's en - ough.
Am
Gm
Coda
Am
Gm
Repeat and Fade

TICKET TO RIDE

Words and Music by JOHN LENNON
and PAUL McCARTNEY

Cm
B♭7
Fm7
E♭
To Coda
1.
She's got a tick-et to ride __ but she don't care. ____ 2. She
2.
A♭7
I don't know why she's rid-ing so high, ____ She ought to
B♭
A♭7
think right, she ought to do right by me. Be-fore she gets to say-ing good-bye, __
B♭
B♭7
D. S. al Coda
She ought to think right, she ought to do right by me. 3. She
Coda
E♭
(tacet)
E♭
My ba-by don't care. My ba-by don't
Repeat and fade

TOMORROW NEVER KNOWS

Words and Music by JOHN LENNON
and PAUL McCARTNEY

shin - ing.
Yet you may see the mean - ing of with - in.
liev - ing.
But lis - ten to the col - or of your dreams:
It is be - ing,
it is be - ing.
It is not leav - ing,
it is not
1.
2.
leav - ing.
So play the game "Ex - ist - ence" to the end,
Fade
of the be - gin - ning,
of the be - gin - ning,
of the be -

WE CAN WORK IT OUT

Words and Music by JOHN LENNON
and PAUL McCARTNEY

Em
Em7
Cmaj7
Em
fight - ing, my friend.
I have al - ways thought
Em7
C6
B7
that it's a crime,
So I will
Em
Em7
Cmaj7
Em
ask you once a - gain.
D. S. al ⊕ Coda
Coda ⊕
C
G
C
D7
G
We can work it out,
We can work it out.
rit.

WHAT YOU'RE DOING

Words and Music by JOHN LENNON
and PAUL McCARTNEY

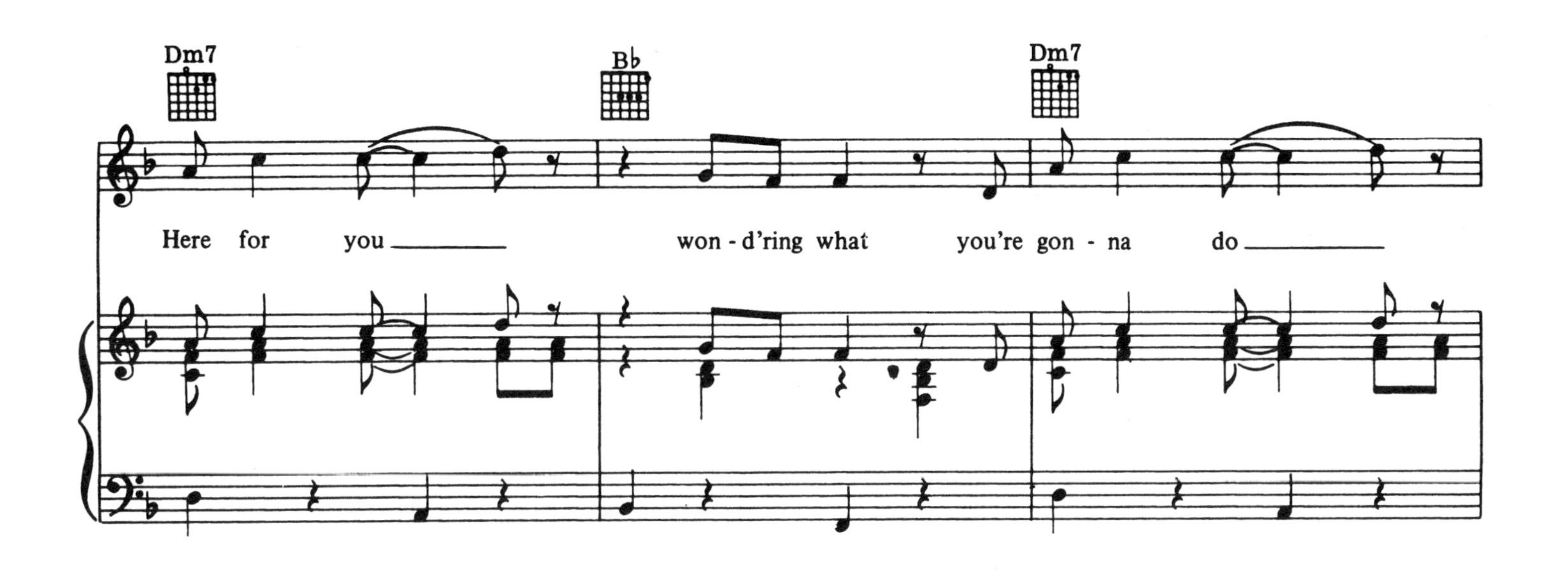
Dm7
Bb
Dm7
Here for you wond-d'ring what you're gon - na do

G7
C7
D.S. al Coda
should you need a love that's true it's me.

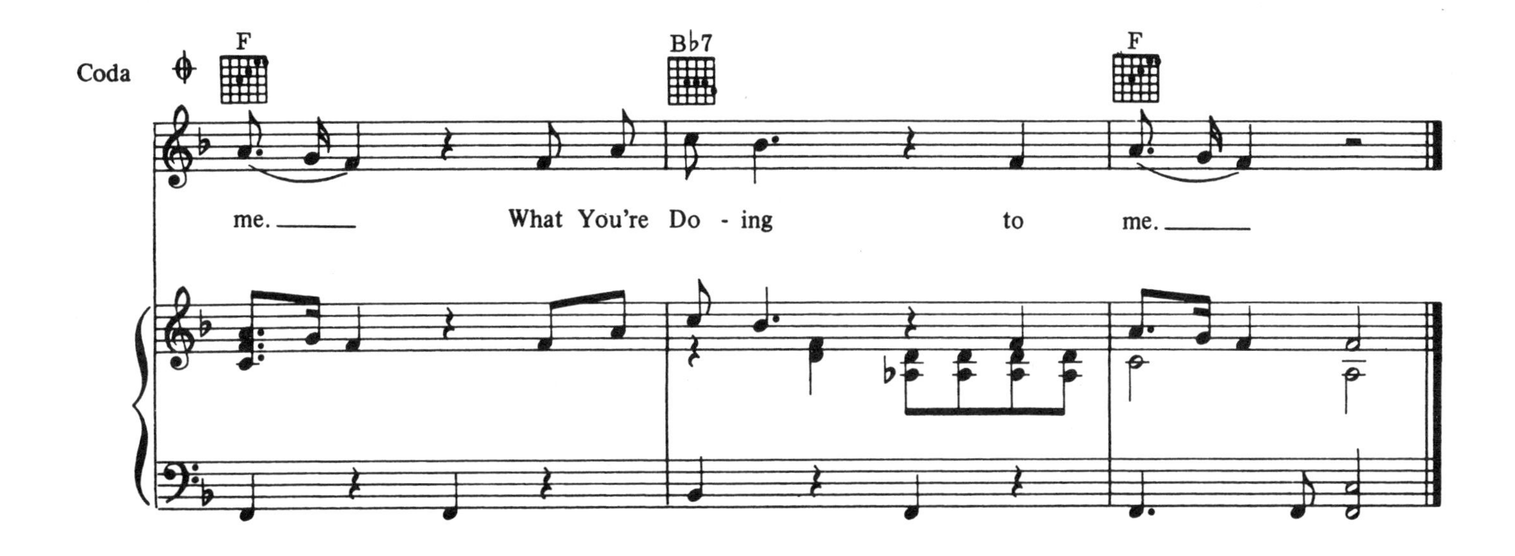
Coda
F
Bb7
F
me. What You're Do - ing to me.

YELLOW SUBMARINE

Words and Music by JOHN LENNON
and PAUL McCARTNEY

CHORUS
G D G
We all live in a yel-low sub-ma-rine, yel-low sub-ma-rine, yel-low sub-ma-rine.
D G
We all live in a yel-low sub-ma-rine, yel-low sub-ma-rine, yel-low sub-ma-rine And our
As we
D C G Em Am Cmaj7 D G
friends are all on board, man-y more of them live next door. And the
live a life of ease ev-'ry one of us has all we need. Sky of
D C G Em Am7 D7 G
1.
band be-gins to play.
blue and sea of
Solo
G Em Am Cmaj7 D7
2.
Repeat Chorus from the D. S. and fade
green in our yel - low sub - ma - rine.

YES IT IS

Words and Music by JOHN LENNON
and PAUL McCARTNEY

F
Dm
Gm7
C7
Am
Am7
you by my side, If I could for-get her but it's my pride, Yes it is, Yes it is, Oh, Yes it
D7
G7
C
F
Dm7
G7
is. Yeh. Please don't wear red to- night,
C
F
Bb6
G7
C
Am
This is what I said to - night. For red is the col - or that will
F
Bb7
Am
C
E
F
G7
C
make me blue in spite of you it's true, Yes it is, it's true, Yes it is, it's true.
rit.

YESTERDAY

Words and Music by JOHN LENNON
and PAUL McCARTNEY

F C Dm G Bb F
o - ver me Oh yes - ter - day came sud - den - ly.
Em7 A7 Dm C Bb Dm Gm C F Em7 A7
Why she had to go I don't know, she would - n't say. I said
Dm C Bb Dm Gm C F F
some - thing wrong now I long for yes - ter - day. Yes - ter - day,
Em7 A7 Dm Dm/C bass Bb C
love was such an eas - y game to play Now I need a place to
F C Dm G Bb F F G Bb F
hide a - way Oh I be - lieve in yes - ter - day. Mm mm mm mm mm.

YOU'VE GOT TO HIDE YOUR LOVE AWAY

Words and Music by JOHN LENNON
and PAUL McCARTNEY

F
C
Eb
F
Bb
Eb
Bb
I can see them laugh at me And I hear them say,
Gath - er 'round, all you clowns, Let me hear you say,
C7
F
Bb
"Hey, you've got to hide your love a -
Gm7
C7
Gm7
C7
way!"
1.
"Hey, you've got to hide your love a - way!"
2.
Repeat and fade out
"Hey, you've got to hide your love a - way!"

WAIT

Words and Music by JOHN LENNON
and PAUL McCARTNEY

F Bb F F+ A7
1. Dm
2. Dm
We'll for - get the tears we cried. But if your I feel as
G7 C7 F
though you ought to know That I've been good as good as I can
Dm G7 C7 F
be, And if you do, I'll trust in you And know that you will wait for
3
Dm A Dm7 G7 Gm Dm A7 Dm
me. It's been a long time, now I'm com-ing back home; I've been a -
But if your heart breaks, Don't wait turn me a - way; And if your

Dm7 G7 Gm Dm A7 Dm F B♭
way now, Oh how I've been a-lone. Wait till I
heart's strong, Hold on I won't de-lay.
F B♭ F B♭ F F+ A7 1. Dm
come back to your side We'll for-get the tears we cried. I feel as
2. Dm Dm7 G7 Gm Dm A7 Dm
It's been a long time, Now I'm com-ing back home; I've been a-
Dm7 G7 Gm Dm A7 Dm
rit.
way now, Oh how I've been a - lone.
rit.